BACK TO THE SLAUGHTERHOUSE

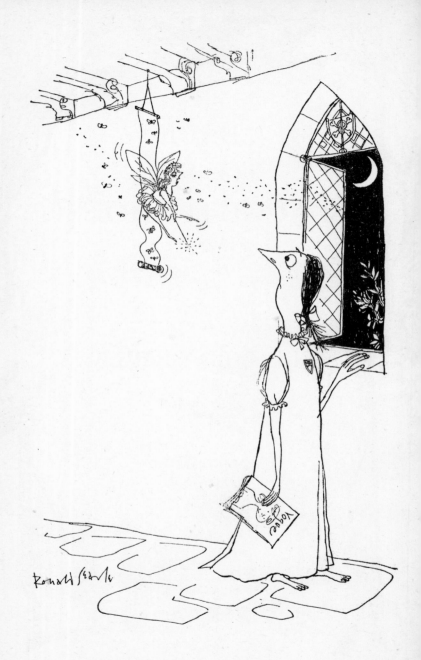

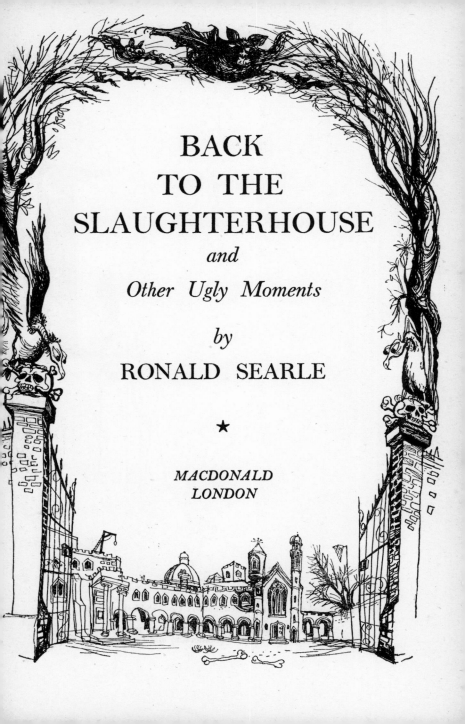

BACK TO THE SLAUGHTERHOUSE

and

Other Ugly Moments

by

RONALD SEARLE

★

MACDONALD
LONDON

Published in 1951 by Macdonald & Co. (Publishers) Ltd.,
16 Maddox Street, W.1.
Made and printed in Great Britain by Purnell and
Sons, Ltd., Paulton (Somerset) and London

FOR MY WIFE
who encourages me
in all this

and

FOR MY CHILDREN
—until they are old enough
to dissociate themselves
from it.

" When, one evening, Dr. Johnson's young friend Mr. Langton, having read aloud to him the first two acts of a very violent tragedy by one of the less well-known Elizabethan dramatists, said rather nervously, 'But I fear, sir, that I weary you. I will read no more.'

Johnson replied, 'No, no, Lanky. Let's go back to the slaughterhouse.'" *Max Beerbohm.*

*　　*　　*　　*　　*

With some unpublished exceptions the drawings in this book have appeared in the pages of *Lilliput, Sunday Express, Punch, Tribune, The Saturday Book, The Sketch, The Leader, World Horizon* and *W. H. Smith's Trade Circular.*

My thanks are due to the editors of these publications for their tolerant co-operation, which has made this collection possible.

R.S.

" *I hear the cost of living is still rising.*"

" ' Escapism ', he says—wants

home and listen to the news."

" *Shhh!* "

[By permission of the proprietors of Punch.

12

" Darling !—just what I wanted ! "

" Psst—short of police? "

" *My dear, if you don't haggle they think you're a tourist.*"

15

TAKING
THE
PLUNGE

Seven Ways of
Entering the Water

Embryonic

Egotistic

Moronic

Domestic

Photogenic

Flop

" *Psst !—want to buy a sonnet ?* "

" Hot, isn't it?"

21

" *If it's any consolation, Sir Alfred Munnings
says a photo-finish isn't art.*"

Ronald Searle

24

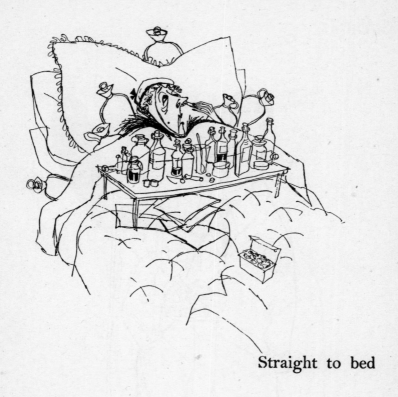

Straight to bed

HOW TO CURE A COLD

*Eight well-tried prescriptions
for handy reference.*

25

An onion morning and night

Mustard bath

Mother Nature's
cure

A good old sweat

Hot grog

Medicated steam

" Bud I habbend godda code ! "

Back to the Slaughterhouse . . .

" Well—you said you loved me."

" I picked it up at Euston."

" . . . and tell Granny I didn't mean to burn her house down."

" *Hell!   My best Scotch.*"

" Life will be empty without you, Drusilla."

" But, Miss Merryweather, you said *we* could bring our pets back with us."

" Fair play, St. Trinian's—use a clean needle."

" And this is Rachel—our head girl."

41

" Smashing !—now pass the bat's blood."

" Go on, make him abolish prep."

"Come along, prefects.   Playtime over."

" Don't be greedy, Cynthia, give your sister some."

46

" Playing with lethal weapons—a boy of your age!"

" Little Maisy's our problem child."

48

" Could you tell me the time, please?"

"Cynthia! How many times must I tell you to take the band off before you light up . . ."

*" It reads, ' Apply match to blue paper
and stand close.' "*

" *Bash her again. I think she moved.*"

" Caught the little beast trying to warn Herbert Morrison."

Christmas Carols

" *First of all we'll list the people who'll
pay us to go away.*"

" O.K. kids. Enough for a pint all round."

" Help me turn her—
she's thawing."

" *Let's give 'em*
Jingle Bells."

" And God bless you, my little darling."

new year resolutions

" . . . to flog them only once a day."

*" We'd better have her examined—she's resolved
to be good."*

" *Go on, say it—' I resolve to leave my body to Science.*' "

" Well done, Cynthia—it was Deadly Nightshade."

The rustle of
Spring

" *Chuck those out—they're harmless.*"

" *It means we must make sacrifices, darling.*
Help Mummy by cutting down your smoking."

Festival
Celebrations

" Yippee !—it's wine ! "

*" Eunice, dear—aren't we rather muddling our
patron saints? "*

69

Delinquency . . .

" We must face facts, men. Is Ava worth the increase—or do we admit the cinema encourages delinquency and take music lessons?"

" Two hours building him a flippin' castle—then he tries to charge me tuppence to look over it."

"*Errol Flynn's started something all right—marrying a girl with glasses.*"

"*See me in the vestry afterwards, Bodkin.*"

71

" Excuse me, your Proust is showing."

. . *The Reading Public*

" Got any comics? "

" *Have you a book on
advanced neurosis?* "

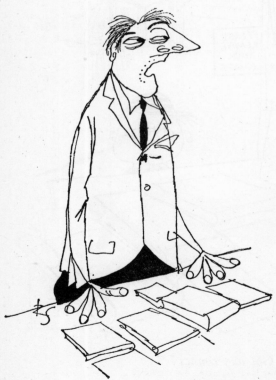

" *I want a copy of
the Picasso play.*"

"*Can you tell me, is this a Book Society Choice?*"

"*No, thanks—I'm just browsing . . . ,*"

THE PRESS AND
ITS READERS

Three embellished statements unashamedly lifted from a Mass-Observation Survey

" I take the 'News of the World' because of the crossword puzzles."
(*Man, civil servant, 44.*)

"All newspapers are the same."
(*Unskilled worker, 44.*)

" I read the ' Pictorial'. I buy it for the baby to look at the pictures."
(*Housewife, unskilled working class, 30.*)

" *She's a flying sorceress—wonders if you'd be interested in the woman's angle.*"

Left, Right...Left, Right...

"*Perhaps His Majesty's Minister is not aware of the grave displeasure with which the Primrose League views the Government's sunflower scheme.*"

"Dear friends, unprepared as I was that I should be called upon to stand for this constituency, it is with sincere . . ."

"Sorry, Missus — 'Suffering under the Socialists' doesn't count for sickness priority."

" It's Winchell, your honour—he says not to worry but there's an International Brigade heading for Congress to fight the Spanish loan."

"*Dearest, why, if the Government is against flogging, do they encourage three line whips in the Commons?*"

"*To me the answer is simple —If they can't get the Government out on Divisions, why don't they try Calculus.*"

. . . and we can say with confidence we are mustering all our resources to capture the floating vote.''

*" Minerals—cigarettes—olive
branches."*

*" He wants us to push it
through. It's a bill to abolish
leftwingers from football."*

84

"We also have this line in blue, sir—specially screened to remove the red element."

" O.K. — No Command Performance! No Royal Film Show! But why can't I be screened by zee Home Office ? "

"Hither, page — see if yon[d]
peasant can wangle a little f[?]
for us off permit."

" I've got a feeling, Mabel, that
if you and me don't do something
about the distribution of our load,
we're going to have our own little
power cut."

"Very well, then. To obviate criticism Cinderella's slipper will be found by an official of the Ministry of Supply."

" I say—are you sure that's Father Christmas? "

"_Bert! Bert! Come up! I'm sure we can manage with logs. Can you hear me? Bert . . . !_"

"_Dear Colleague. Owing to the repeal of the 1735 Witch-craft Act we have pleasure in offering at reduced rates our Refresher Course in flying . . ._"

" . . . and this, children, is where they work for peace."

Ronald Searle

"Jenkins, I want you to get me one of those new long-playing records which 'give up to half an hour of continuous enjoyment'."

LOVE: A Survey

Verses by Kaye Webb

with acknowledgements

to the obvious sources . . .

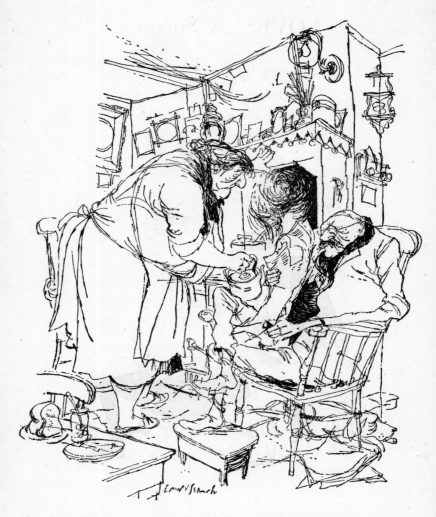

TRADITIONAL: *or Thank the Lord it's nearly over.*

Say I'm weary; say I'm sad;
Say that health and wealth have missed me.
And if you seek a reason—add
Jenny kissed me.

92

FINANCIAL: *or I'm proud of my little girl.*

She has a charge account at Fortnum's,
Her bank book never shows a red,
Her life assurance dues are paid for,
And, take a look, he's nearly dead.

VENAL: *or love in W.2.*

Maisie's a blonde, dilly dilly,
My true love was red,
But when it gets dark, dilly dally,
She'll do instead.

EXPERIMENTAL: *or c'est le premier pas qui coûte.*

> The sky is blew, baby,
> You are trew, baby,
> And I know what to dew, baby,
> But, baby, " it's cold outside ".